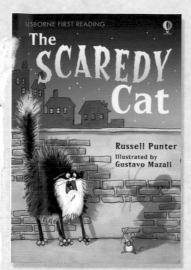

USBORNE FIRST READING

The SCAREDY Cat

Russell Punter
Illustrated by
Gustavo Mazali

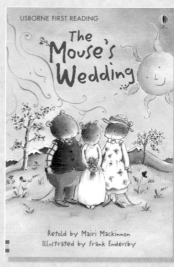

USBORNE FIRST READING

The Mouse's Wedding

Retold by Mairi Mackinnon
Illustrated by Frank Endersby

USBORNE FIRST READING

The Magic Porridge Pot

Based on the story by The Brothers Grimm
Illustrated by Mike and Carl Gordon

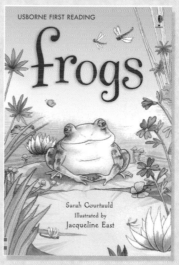

USBORNE FIRST READING

frogs

Sarah Courtauld
Illustrated by
Jacqueline East

Androcles
and the
Lion

Based on a story by Aesop

Retold by
Russell Punter

Illustrated by

Mike and Carl Gordon

Reading Consultant: Alison Kelly
Roehampton University

A long time ago, there was a man called Androcles*.

He was very poor...

but he was kind.

*say And-rock-lees

Androcles worked for a rich man named Brutus*.

Brutus lived in a big house outside the city of Rome.

3

*say Broo-tus

Brutus made his slaves
work hard. Every day,
Androcles scrubbed
steps...

mopped
floors...

made beds...

But Brutus never paid him.
All Androcles got was one
piece of dry bread a day.

Even the birds won't eat this.

One night, Androcles decided to run away. He climbed through a window.

Then he ran into the forest.

Androcles had never been in the forest before. It was dark and spooky.

Gulp!

Suddenly, he heard a loud
noise from behind a bush.

RAAAAGGGGH!

Androcles jumped. "Who...
who's there?" he asked.

9

He looked around the bush
and saw...

RAAAAGGGGH!

an **enormous** lion.
Androcles ran.

But the lion didn't run
after Androcles. He sat there,
as still as stone.

Androcles was surprised.
He went back. "Why didn't
you chase me?" he asked.

"I can't run," sniffed the lion. "I can't even walk. There's a thorn in my paw."

It really stings.

"You poor thing," said Androcles. "Let me help."

12

He gripped the thorn.
"This might hurt."

I can't look.

Androcles pulled out the
thorn, as quickly as he could.

13

"Oooch!" yelped the lion.
"All done," said Androcles.

"Thank you!" cried the lion
happily. "I'm Leo."
14

He smiled and gave
Androcles a big, sloppy lick.

Slluuuurp!

From then on, Androcles
and Leo were best friends.

They lived in a cave in the middle of the forest.

They hunted for food every day,

and, each night, they shared it.

One morning, Androcles
saw a stranger.

He tip-toed closer.

"A soldier!" he thought.
"What does he want?"

The soldier unrolled some
paper. Androcles gasped.

Just then, Androcles felt a
bug on his nose. It tickled.

19

"Hey!" cried the soldier.
"Stop right there!"

20

The soldier pulled out
his sword.

Help!

Androcles ran.

The soldier chased
Androcles between
bushes...

up hills...

down hills...

across a stream...

around

trees...

and out of
the forest.

Androcles got so tired,
he had to stop.

The soldier threw Androcles
into a cart.

"Are you taking me back to
Brutus?" panted Androcles.

24

"No," boomed the soldier.
"You're going to Rome."

"Why?" asked Androcles.
"You'll see," the soldier said.

Androcles had a bumpy
ride to Rome. The city was
crowded and noisy.

He had never seen so many people.

Then he noticed a big, round building. "What's that?" he asked.

"It's the arena*," said the soldier. "That's where you're going."

28

*say a-ree-na

"What happens there?"
asked Androcles.

"You'll see," the soldier said.

29

A man called Clinkus
pulled Androcles off the cart.

Out you get,
skinny!

He led Androcles into the
arena, past a cage of lions.

They weren't as gentle
as Leo.

ROAR! SNARL!

Yikes!

"Why are they here?"
Androcles asked nervously.
"You'll see," said Clinkus.

Androcles was locked in
a prison with a man called
Marco.

"What happens now?"
asked Androcles.

"We fight in the arena,"
said Marco.

"But I don't want to fight
you," said Androcles.

"We don't fight each
other..." Marco sighed.

"We fight the lions."

Androcles gulped.

We'll be torn to pieces!

"Everyone in Rome comes
to watch," said Marco. "Even
the Emperor."

"Our fights are tomorrow afternoon," he added.

Androcles and Marco didn't get much sleep that night.

35

The next afternoon,
Clinkus dragged Androcles
from the prison.

He took him down a long,
dark tunnel to a doorway.

Clinkus pushed Androcles
through the door.

Put up a
good fight!

Androcles stood in the
middle of the arena.

A gate opened in a side wall, and an **enormous** lion charged out.

Androcles trembled with fear. There was nowhere to run.

Androcles closed his eyes.
"I hope it's over quickly,"
he thought.

Then something strange
happened...

Androcles felt a lick on his hand. He opened his eyes to see... Leo!

"I was caught last night," said Leo. "They brought me here to fight."

Androcles hugged his friend.
The crowd couldn't believe it.

"Androcles has tamed the lion," they cried. "What a hero!"

Androcles!

Androcles!

Clinkus took Androcles to the Emperor.

"You were very brave,"
said the Emperor. "I think I'll
set you free."

Androcles thought of his
friends. "Please will you free
Marco and the lion too?"

The Emperor smiled.
"Very well," he said.

My hero!

Androcles and his friends
left Rome and started their
own show.

And no one had to fight.

Androcles and the Lion is based on one of
Aesop's Fables. These are a collection
of short stories, told in Greece about
4,000 years ago. The stories always
have a moral (a message or lesson) at
the end. The moral of this story is:
be kind to your friends and they will
never forget you.

Series editor: Lesley Sims

First published in 2008 by Usborne Publishing Ltd., Usborne House,
83-85 Saffron Hill, London EC1N 8RT, England. www.usborne.com
Copyright © 2008 Usborne Publishing Ltd.

USBORNE FIRST READING
Level Four

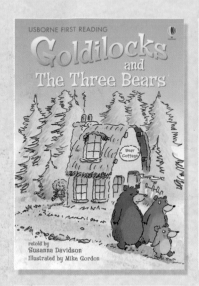

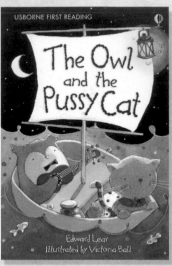

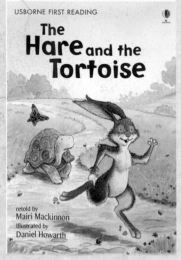

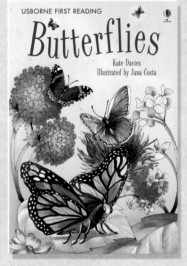

Looking at Countries

FRANCE

Jillian Powell

FRANKLIN WATTS

LONDON·SYDNEY

First published in 2006 by
Franklin Watts
338 Euston Road
London NW1 3BH

Franklin Watts Australia
Level 17/207 Kent Street
Sydney NSW 2000

ISBN: 978 0 7496 6474 9
Dewey classification: 914.4

Series editor: Sarah Peutrill
Art director: Jonathan Hair
Design: Rita Storey
Cover design: Peter Scoulding
Picture research: Diana Morris

Picture credits: Eric Brading/Alamy: 13. Dex Images/Corbis: 23.
Bernd Ducke/Superbild/A1 Pix: 26c. Owen Franken/Corbis: 12, 17.
Gunter Gräfenhain/Superbild/A1 Pix: 8. Shaun Greenfield.
Photography/Photographers Direct: 11. HAGA/Superbild/A1 Pix: 27.
Chris Hellier/Corbis: 19. John Heseltine/Corbis: 21b. Roger G
Howard/Photographers Direct: 16. Incolor/Superbild/A1 Pix: 7t.
Buddy Mays/Photographers Direct: 20. Frederic Pitchal/Sygma/Corbis:
22. E. Poupinet/Superbild/A1 Pix: front cover inset,1,14. Roy
Rainford/Robert Harding: 6, 7b. Walter Rawlings/Robert Harding:
front cover main, 21t. Sayama/Superbild/A1 Pix:9. Peter
Scholey/Robert Harding: 4. Alex Segre/Photographers Direct: 25.
Sygma/Corbis: 26bl. Guy Thouvenin/Robert Harding: 18. Horacio
Villalobos/Corbis: 10. Visa Image/Robert Harding: 25c. Tim de
Waele/Corbis: 24. Adam Woolfitt/Corbis: 15. Every attempt has been
made to clear copyright. Should there be any inadvertent omission
please apply to the publisher for rectification.

A CIP catalogue record for this book is available from the British
Library.

Printed in China

Franklin Watts is a division of Hachette Children's Books.

Contents

Where is France? 4

The landscape 6

Weather and seasons 8

French people 10

Home and school 12

Country 14

City 16

French homes 18

Food 20

At work 22

Having fun 24

France: the facts 26

Glossary 28

Find out more 29

Some French words 30

My map of France 31

Index 32

Where is France?

France is in the west of Europe and has borders with eight other European countries.

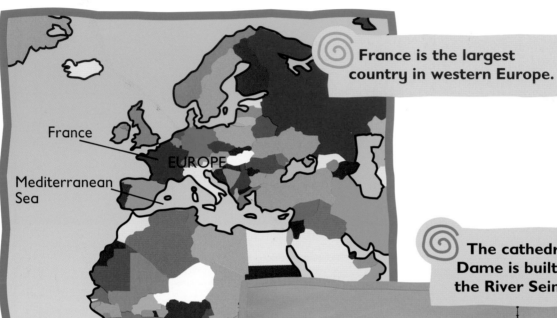

France

EUROPE

Mediterranean Sea

France is the largest country in western Europe.

The cathedral of Nôtre Dame is built on an island in the River Seine in Paris.

Paris is the capital city of France. It was built along the River Seine and has many famous old buildings like the Eiffel Tower and Nôtre Dame cathedral.

France has a long coastline by the Atlantic Ocean and the Mediterranean Sea. It is joined to Great Britain by a tunnel under the English Channel.

Use this map to find the places mentioned in this book.

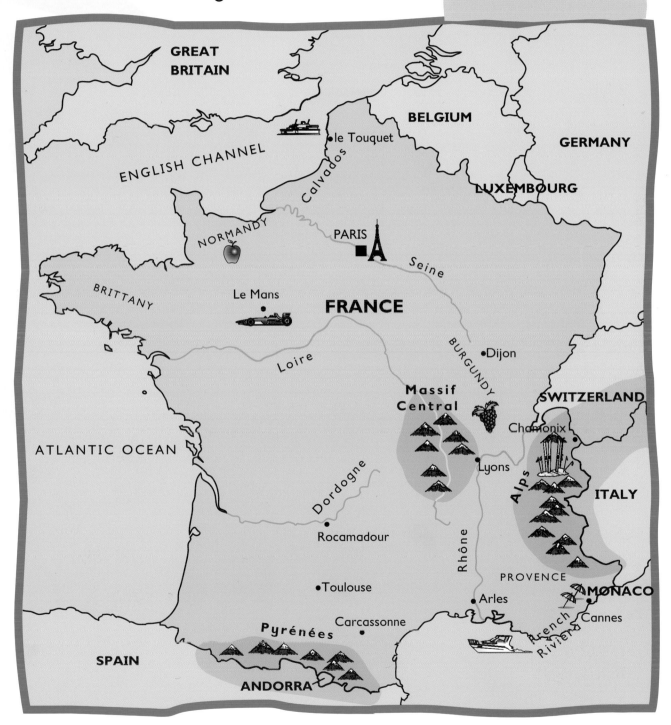

GREAT BRITAIN

ENGLISH CHANNEL

BELGIUM

GERMANY

le Touquet

LUXEMBOURG

Calvados

NORMANDY

PARIS

Seine

BRITTANY

Le Mans

FRANCE

Loire

BURGUNDY

Dijon

Massif Central

SWITZERLAND

Chamonix

ATLANTIC OCEAN

Lyons

Alps

ITALY

Dordogne

Rhône

Rocamadour

PROVENCE

Toulouse

Arles

MONACO

Carcassonne

Cannes

Pyrénées

French Riviera

SPAIN

ANDORRA

The landscape

France has a beautiful and varied landscape. It has gentle hills, flat plains and river valleys, as well as high mountain ranges like the Pyrénées and the Alps. The coastline in the south has salt flats and wetlands as well as sandy beaches.

The hill town of Rocamadour is popular with tourists.

Poplar trees line roads and rivers running through the rich farmland of the northwest.

Did you know?

More than a quarter of France is covered with forest. Wild boar still live in some forests.

Many tourists visit France to enjoy the countryside or fine beaches in the south or west of the country.

The sunny south coast is known as the French Riviera.

Weather and seasons

Most of France has cool winters and warm sunny summers. The coldest winters are in mountains like the Alps, where heavy snow falls.

Winter snow makes Chamonix near Mont Blanc popular for sports such as skiing and snowboarding.

Lavender grows well in the hot sunny climate of Provence in the south.

The south has a Mediterranean climate, with mild winters and hot, dry summers. Summer drought can lead to forest fires. Rain falls mainly in the spring and autumn, and sometimes a cold wind called the Mistral blows down the Rhône valley.

Did you know?

The Mistral sometimes blows so hard that it damages fields of crops.

French people

This Roman Catholic woman is lighting a candle in her church.

The people of France are a mix of different cultures. They include people who have moved there from the Middle East, Portugal, Russia, Asia and North Africa.

There are many different religions. Many people are Roman Catholic, but there are also Protestants, Muslims and Jews.

The French are proud of their country's history and language. Each region, or *pays*, of France has its own traditional costume and food. Some people still speak local languages like Basque and Catalan near the Spanish border, and Breton in Brittany. French is spoken everywhere.

Did you know?

French is spoken in 21 other countries around the world.

A local farmers' market in the Dordogne region. Popular regional foods can be bought here.

Home and school

Home and family life are important to French people. They enjoy spending time together, sitting down to share meals every day and meeting up with relatives on special occasions such as birthdays and weddings.

Did you know?

France has over 100 daily newspapers.

Children in France are given presents and cards on their birthday.

French children do not have to wear school uniforms.

French children must start school when they are six and leave between the ages of 16 and 18. The school day starts at 8.30 am and finishes at 5.30 pm. There is a two-hour break for lunch when children eat at school or at home. Some children have Wednesday afternoons free for sports or youth clubs, but many go to school on Saturday mornings.

Country

About a quarter of French people live in the country, in villages or small market towns. As more people have moved away to the cities to find work, many country and farm houses have become second homes for city people or holiday homes for tourists.

Grapes have been grown in France for over 1,000 years. Burgundy is in central east France and is one of many wine-making regions.

Old houses in Calvados in the region of Normandy, northern France.

French market towns usually have a main square, a church, a town hall and some small shops with an open-air market once a week. Many of the houses are hundreds of years old.

Did you know?

France is one of the least crowded countries in Europe.

City

There are almost as many scooters and motorcycles as cars in France.

Most people in France live in towns or big cities. The capital city, Paris, is the largest city in France. It has fashionable shops, cafés and restaurants as well as art galleries, museums, offices and factories.

Paris has an underground train system called *Le Métro*, which is short for *Métropolitain*.

Did you know?

In central Paris, every building is within 500 metres of a Métro station.

Paris is a centre for finance and for the fashion industry, with designer shows attracting people from all over the world. Cannes, a city on the Mediterranean coast, is famous for the international film festival held each year. Other cities are important for local industries, like cloth-making in Lyons or aircraft manufacture in Toulouse.

French homes

Many French people live in blocks of apartments in the suburbs of cities and travel in to the city to work. Some apartment blocks are over 100 years old. Others are newly built.

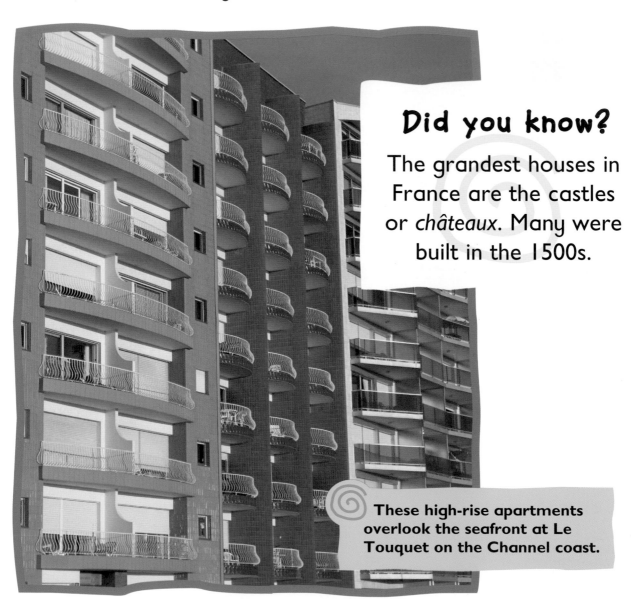

Did you know?

The grandest houses in France are the castles or *châteaux*. Many were built in the 1500s.

These high-rise apartments overlook the seafront at Le Touquet on the Channel coast.

Old terraced houses in Arles in Provence, which has many buildings from Roman and Medieval times.

Older houses in towns and villages often have clay-tiled or slate roofs and shutters at the windows. They are usually built from stone or have wooden frames. Some are built in terraces and have three or more storeys.

Food

France is famous for good food and cooking. Most people shop at supermarkets each week but they also buy fresh foods from street markets and small shops such as cheese shops, cake shops and bakeries.

French people like to buy bread and other fresh foods daily.

French restaurants and cafés often have tables for eating and drinking outside.

Did you know?

The French make over 400 types of cheese, with milk from goats, sheep or cows.

Many regions have their own produce and dishes, like *crêpes* from Brittany, mustard from Dijon, and fish soups and stews from Provence.

Normandy is famous for dishes using local apples and cream.

At work

French cars are sold all over the world.

Many French people work in banks, shops, offices and schools. Others work in factories, making cars, perfumes, wines or cheeses that are sold worldwide. The main industries include machinery, transport equipment and electronics.

Tourism provides many jobs in Paris and in other historic cities and towns as well as coastal resorts.

Did you know?

Over 60 million tourists visit France each year, making it one of the world's most popular holiday destinations.

A waiter in a restaurant in the historic walled city of Carcassonne.

Having fun

The French enjoy sports including football, tennis and cycling. France hosts international events like the French Open tennis tournament, motor-racing at Le Mans and the *Tour de France* cycling race.

Cyclists from all over the world compete in the *Tour de France.*

Boules or *Pétanque* is played in town and village squares all over France.

Many French people enjoy playing games such as *boules*. They also enjoy the arts such as cinema, theatre and art shows.

A woman wearing Breton costume for a feast day in Brittany.

Did you know?

There are over 400 French festivals: some celebrate foods such as snails, sausages or frogs' legs.

The French celebrate national holidays and festivals all through the year. People like to dress up in traditional costume, and celebrate with singing, dancing and feasting.

France: the facts

• Nearly 61 million people live in France today. Over two million people live in the capital city, Paris.

• France is a republic. The president is the head of state and the prime minister leads the government.

• The island of Corsica, and overseas territories such as Guadaloupe and Martinique are also part of France.

The French use the European currency, euros and cents.

The French flag is called *le tricolore* (the three-colour). It has stripes of blue, white and red.

• France is a member state of the European Union.

The Eiffel Tower in Paris, lit up with fireworks celebrating the day when France became a republic, on 14 July 1790.

Did you know?

The name France comes from the Franks, the people who lived there after the Roman Empire.

Glossary

Apartment a home in a block of flats.

Capital city the most important city in a country.

Channel Tunnel a tunnel that runs under the English Channel linking France and Britain.

Crêpe a type of pancake.

Drought a long period without rain.

Electronics describes the industry that makes electronic goods and parts.

Medieval times the period between the fifth and fifteenth centuries.

Mediterranean climate a climate of mild winters and warm summers, in countries bordering the Mediterranean Sea.

Mistral a cold wind that blows from the north in southern France.

Pays the French name for a region within the country.

Republic a country with no king or queen, where decision-making power is held by the people and their representatives.

Roman from the city and culture of Rome; the Roman Empire lasted from the sixth century BCE to the fifth century CE.

Salt flats flat, salty land near the sea.

Suburbs the area on the edge of a town or city.

Town hall a building that is the centre of local government.

Wetlands low, marshy land.

Wild boar a kind of wild pig that lives in forests.

Find out more

About France:
oxfam.org.uk/coolplanet/ont heline/explore/journey/france
A virtual journey through France, with young French people talking about their lives.

www.info-france-usa.org/kids
A website for children produced by the French embassy in the United States with lots of information on topics including arts, education and sports, plus interactive games.

Learning French:
www.bbc.co.uk/schools/ primaryfrench
The BBC website has flash animated cartoons with a soundtrack to help pronunciation.

www.primaryfrench.co.uk
An award winning fun website produced by a French club in the UK with sections on words including numbers, colours and animals.

Note to parents and teachers: Every effort has been made by the Publishers to ensure that these websites are suitable for children, that they are of the highest educational value, and that they contain no inappropriate or offensive material. However, because of the nature of the Internet, it is impossible to guarantee that the contents of these sites will not be altered. We strongly advise that Internet access is supervised by a responsible adult.

Some French words

French word	English word	Say ...
au revoir	goodbye, see you again	oh-re-vwar
bonjour	hello / good day	bo-zhoor
la fête	festival	la fate
je m'appelle	my name is	zhe mah-pehl
je m'excuse	I'm sorry	je m'excuse
l'école	school	l'aykol
la famille	family	la fah-meey
la maison	house	la mehzon
le magasin	shop	le magazan
les français	the French	lay fronseh
merci	thank you	mehr-see
non	no	non
oui	yes	wee
s'il vous plaît	please	seel voo pleh

My map of France

Trace this map, colour it in and use the map on page 5 to write the names of all the places.

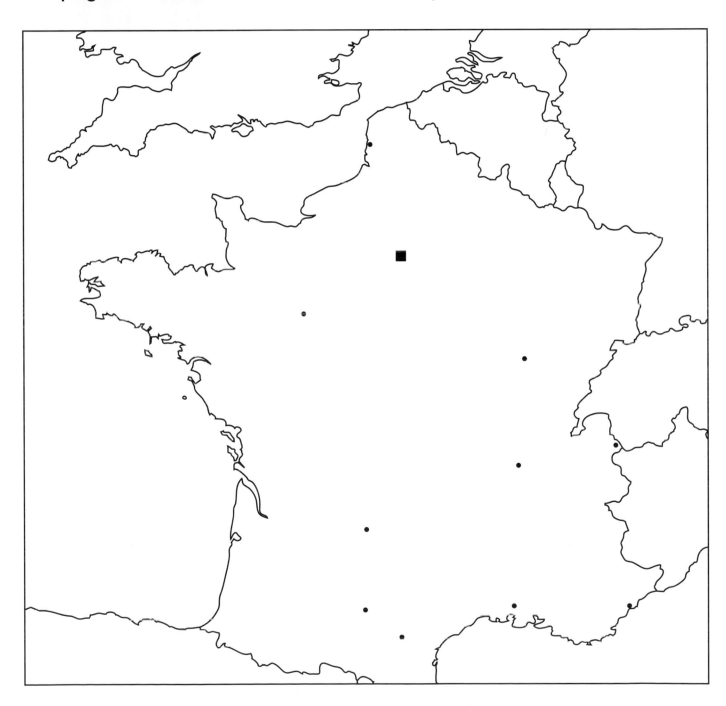

Index

beaches 6, 7
birthdays 13

capital city 4, 16, 26, 28
castles 18
costume 11, 25
country 14–15
cultures 10
currency 26

Eiffel Tower 4, 27

family 12
farming 7, 14
festivals 25
flag 26
food 11, 20–21, 25
forests 7, 9
French Riveria 7

homes 18-19

industry 17, 22

landscape 6–7
language 11, 30

mountains 6, 8

Paris 4, 5, 16, 17, 23, 26, 27

religion 10
rivers 4, 5, 6, 7

school 13
seasons 8–9
sport 8, 13, 24, 25, 29

tourism 6, 7, 14, 23
towns 15

weather 8–9
work 22–23